THIS ADDRESS BOOK BELONGS TO... Julie R

ADDRESS Graigue, Hayden,
Callan,
Co. Kilkenny

TELEPHONE 7769219

MOBILE PHONE

EMAIL

First publishing in Great Britain in 2001
Bloomsbury Publishing Plc, 38 Soho Square, London, W1D 3HB

ISBN 0 7475 5505 2

Designed by Traffika Publishing Ltd.
Printed in China by Leo Paper Products

ADDRESS BOOK

Welcome

Addresses

Name

Address

Tel Fax

Mobile

Email

Name

Address

Tel Fax

Mobile

Email

Name

Address

Tel Fax

Mobile

Email

Addresses

Name

Address

Tel Fax

Mobile

Email

Name

Address

Tel Fax

Mobile

Email

Name

Address

Tel Fax

Mobile

Email

Addresses

Name

Address

Tel Fax

Mobile

Email

Name

Address

Tel Fax

Mobile

Email

Addresses

Name

Address

Tel Fax

Mobile

Email

Name

Address

Tel Fax

Mobile

Email

Name

Address

Tel Fax

Mobile

Email

Addresses

Name

Address

Tel Fax

Mobile

Email

Name

Address

Tel Fax

Mobile

Email

Name

Address

Tel Fax

Mobile

Email

Addresses

Name

Address

Tel Fax

Mobile

Email

Name

Address

Tel Fax

Mobile

Email

Name

Address

Tel Fax

Mobile

Email

Name

Address

Tel Fax

Mobile

Email

Name

Address

Tel Fax

Mobile

Email

Addresses

Name

Address

Tel Fax

Mobile

Email

Name

Address

Tel Fax

Mobile

Email

Name

Address

Tel Fax

Mobile

Email

Addresses

Name

Address

Tel Fax

Mobile

Email

Name

Address

Tel Fax

Mobile

Email

Name

Address

Tel Fax

Mobile

Email

Addresses

Name

Address

Tel Fax

Mobile

Email

Name

Address

Tel Fax

Mobile

Email

Name

Address

Tel Fax

Mobile

Email

Addresses

Name

Address

Tel Fax

Mobile

Email

Name

Address

Tel Fax

Mobile

Email

Addresses

Name

Address

Tel Fax

Mobile

Email

Name

Address

Tel Fax

Mobile

Email

Name

Address

Tel Fax

Mobile

Email

Addresses

Name

Address

Tel Fax

Mobile

Email

Name

Address

Tel Fax

Mobile

Email

Name

Address

Tel Fax

Mobile

Email

Addresses

Name

Address

Tel Fax

Mobile

Email

Name

Address

Tel Fax

Mobile

Email

Name

Address

Tel Fax

Mobile

Email

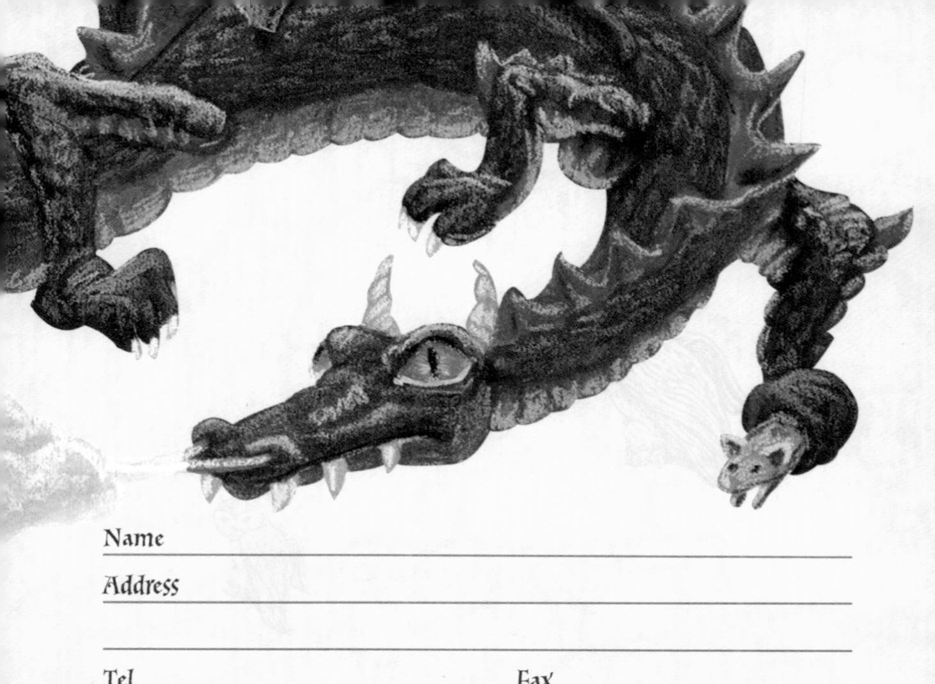

Name

Address

Tel Fax

Mobile

Email

Name

Address

Tel Fax

Mobile

Email

Addresses

Name

Address

Tel Fax

Mobile

Email

Addresses

Name

Address

Tel Fax

Mobile

Email

Name

Address

Tel Fax

Mobile

Email

Name

Address

Tel Fax

Mobile

Email

Addresses

Name

Address

Tel Fax

Mobile

Email

Name

Address

Tel Fax

Mobile

Email

Name

Address

Tel Fax

Mobile

Email

Addresses

Name

Address

Tel Fax

Mobile

Email

Name

Address

Tel Fax

Mobile

Email

Name

Address

Tel Fax

Mobile

Email

Addresses

Name

Address

Tel Fax

Mobile

Email

Name

Address

Tel Fax

Mobile

Email

Name

Address

Tel Fax

Mobile

Email

Addresses

Name

Address

Tel Fax

Mobile

Email

Name

Address

Tel Fax

Mobile

Email

Addresses

Name

Address

Tel Fax

Mobile

Email

Name

Address

Tel Fax

Mobile

Email

Name

Address

Tel Fax

Mobile

Email

Addresses

Name

Address

Tel Fax

Mobile

Email

Name

Address

Tel Fax

Mobile

Email

Name

Address

Tel Fax

Mobile

Email

Addresses

Name

Address

Tel Fax

Mobile

Email

Name

Address

Tel Fax

Mobile

Email

Name

Address

Tel Fax

Mobile

Email

Name

Address

Tel Fax

Mobile

Email

Name

Address

Tel Fax

Mobile

Email

Addresses

Name

Address

Tel Fax

Mobile

Email

Name

Address

Tel Fax

Mobile

Email

Addresses

Name

Address

Tel Fax

Mobile

Email

Name

Address

Tel Fax

Mobile

Email

Name

Address

Tel Fax

Mobile

Email

Addresses

Name

Address

Tel Fax

Mobile

Email

Name

Address

Tel Fax

Mobile

Email

Name

Address

Tel Fax

Mobile

Email

Addresses

Name

Address

Tel Fax

Mobile

Email

Name

Address

Tel Fax

Mobile

Email

Addresses

Name

Address

Tel Fax

Mobile

Email

Name

Address

Tel Fax

Mobile

Email

Name

Address

Tel Fax

Mobile

Email

Addresses

Name

Address

Tel Fax

Mobile

Email

Name

Address

Tel Fax

Mobile

Email

Name

Address

Tel Fax

Mobile

Email

Addresses

Name

Address

Tel Fax

Mobile

Email

Name

Address

Tel Fax

Mobile

Email

Name

Address

Tel Fax

Mobile

Email

Name

Address

Tel Fax

Mobile

Email

Name

Address

Tel Fax

Mobile

Email

Addresses

Name

Address

Tel Fax

Mobile

Email

Addresses

Name

Address

Tel Fax

Mobile

Email

Name

Address

Tel Fax

Mobile

Email

Name

Address

Tel Fax

Mobile

Email

Addresses

Name

Address

Tel Fax

Mobile

Email

Name

Address

Tel Fax

Mobile

Email

Name

Address

Tel Fax

Mobile

Email

Addresses

Name

Address

Tel Fax

Mobile

Email

Name

Address

Tel Fax

Mobile

Email

Name

Address

Tel Fax

Mobile

Email

Addresses

Name

Address

Tel Fax

Mobile

Email

Name

Address

Tel Fax

Mobile

Email

Name

Address

Tel Fax

Mobile

Email

Addresses

Name

Address

Tel Fax

Mobile

Email

Name

Address

Tel Fax

Mobile

Email

HP

Addresses

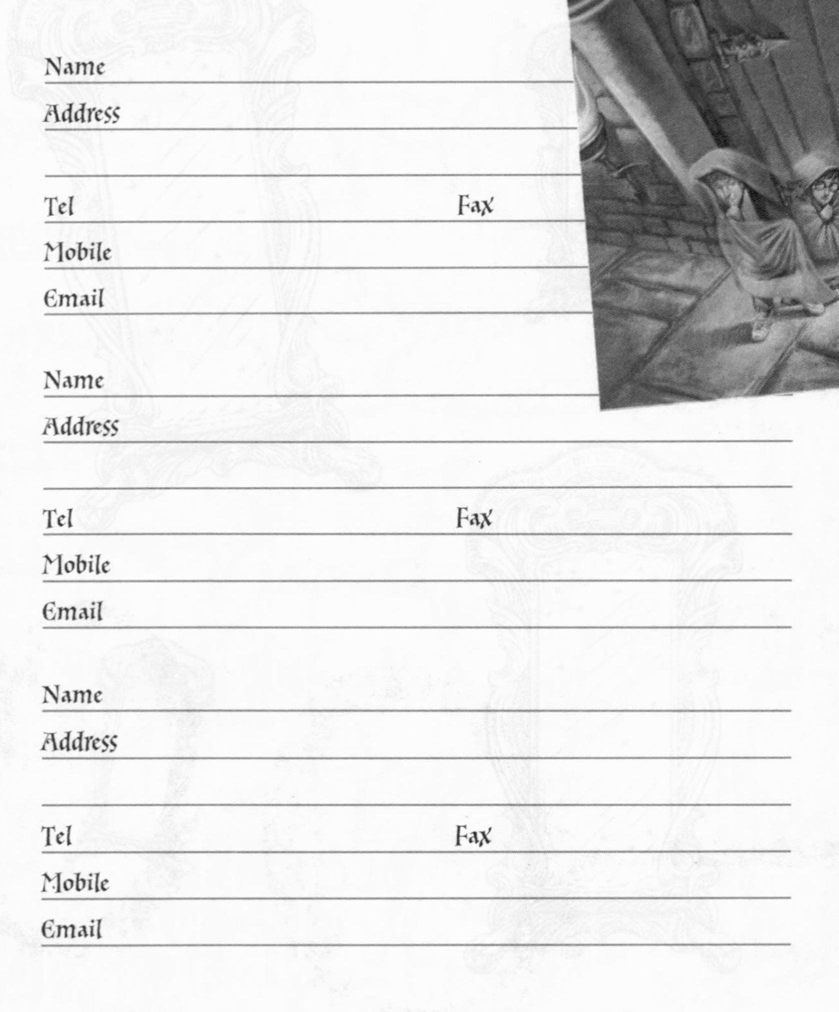

Name

Address

Tel Fax

Mobile

Email

Name

Address

Tel Fax

Mobile

Email

Name

Address

Tel Fax

Mobile

Email

Addresses

Name

Address

Tel Fax

Mobile

Email

Name

Address

Tel Fax

Mobile

Email

Name

Address

Tel Fax

Mobile

Email

Addresses

Name

Address

Tel Fax

Mobile

Email

Name

Address

Tel Fax

Mobile

Email

Name

Address

Tel Fax

Mobile

Email

Name

Address

Tel Fax

Mobile

Email

Name

Address

Tel Fax

Mobile

Email

Addresses

Name

Address

Tel Fax

Mobile

Email

Name

Address

Tel Fax

Mobile

Email

Addresses

Name

Address

Tel Fax

Mobile

Email

Name

Address

Tel Fax

Mobile

Email

Name

Address

Tel Fax

Mobile

Email

Addresses

Name

Address

Tel Fax

Mobile

Email

Name

Address

Tel Fax

Mobile

Email

Name

Address

Tel Fax

Mobile

Email

Addresses

Name

Address

Tel Fax

Mobile

Email

Name

Address

Tel Fax

Mobile

Email

Addresses

Name

Address

Tel Fax

Mobile

Email

Name

Address

Tel Fax

Mobile

Email

Name

Address

Tel Fax

Mobile

Email

Addresses

Name

Address

Tel Fax

Mobile

Email

Name

Address

Tel Fax

Mobile

Email

Name

Address

Tel Fax

Mobile

Email

Addresses

Name

Address

Tel Fax

Mobile

Email

Name

Address

Tel Fax

Mobile

Email

Name

Address

Tel Fax

Mobile

Email

Name

Address

Tel Fax

Mobile

Email

Name

Address

Tel Fax

Mobile

Email

Addresses

Name

Address

Tel Fax

Mobile

Email

J

Addresses

Name

Address

Tel Fax

Mobile

Email

Name

Address

Tel Fax

Mobile

Email

Name

Address

Tel Fax

Mobile

Email

Addresses

Name

Address

Tel Fax

Mobile

Email

Name

Address

Tel Fax

Mobile

Email

Name

Address

Tel Fax

Mobile

Email

Addresses

Name Kathy Robinson
Address Craigue Hayden, Callan

Tel Fax
Mobile
Email

Name
Address

Tel Fax
Mobile
Email

Name
Address

Tel Fax
Mobile
Email

Addresses

Name

Address

Tel Fax

Mobile

Email

Name

Address

Tel Fax

Mobile

Email

Name

Address

Tel Fax

Mobile

Email

Addresses

Name

Address

Tel Fax

Mobile

Email

Name

Address

Tel Fax

Mobile

Email

Addresses

Name

Address

Tel Fax

Mobile

Email

Name

Address

Tel Fax

Mobile

Email

Name

Address

Tel Fax

Mobile

Email

Addresses

Name

Address

Tel Fax

Mobile

Email

Name

Address

Tel Fax

Mobile

Email

Name

Address

Tel Fax

Mobile

Email

Addresses

Name

Address

Tel Fax

Mobile

Email

Name

Address

Tel Fax

Mobile

Email

Name

Address

Tel Fax

Mobile

Email

Name

Address

Tel Fax

Mobile

Email

Name

Address

Tel Fax

Mobile

Email

Addresses

Name

Address

Tel Fax

Mobile

Email

Name

Address

Tel Fax

Mobile

Email

L

HP

Addresses

Name

Address

Tel Fax

Mobile

Email

Name

Address

Tel Fax

Mobile

Email

Name

Address

Tel Fax

Mobile

Email

M

Addresses

Name

Address

Tel Fax

Mobile

Email

Name

Address

Tel Fax

Mobile

Email

Name

Address

Tel Fax

Mobile

Email

Addresses

Name

Address

Tel Fax

Mobile

Email

Name

Address

Tel Fax

Mobile

Email

M

Addresses

Name

Address

Tel Fax

Mobile

Email

Name

Address

Tel Fax

Mobile

Email

Name

Address

Tel Fax

Mobile

Email

Addresses

Name

Address

Tel Fax

Mobile

Email

Name

Address

Tel Fax

Mobile

Email

Name

Address

Tel Fax

Mobile

Email

M

Addresses

Name

Address

Tel Fax

Mobile

Email

Name

Address

Tel Fax

Mobile

Email

Name

Address

Tel Fax

Mobile

Email

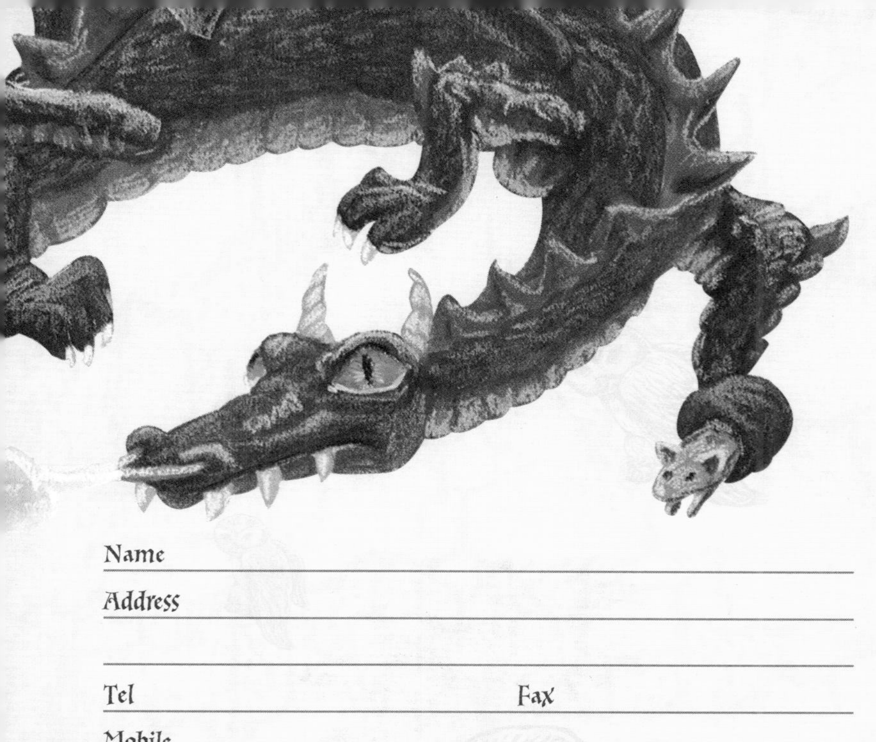

Name

Address

Tel Fax

Mobile

Email

Name

Address

Tel Fax

Mobile

Email

N

Addresses

Name

Address

Tel Fax

Mobile

Email

N

Addresses

Name

Address

Tel Fax

Mobile

Email

Name

Address

Tel Fax

Mobile

Email

Name

Address

Tel Fax

Mobile

Email

N

Addresses

Name

Address

Tel Fax

Mobile

Email

Name

Address

Tel Fax

Mobile

Email

N

Name

Address

Tel Fax

Mobile

Email

Addresses

Name

Address

Tel Fax

Mobile

Email

Name

Address

Tel Fax

Mobile

Email

Name

Address

Tel Fax

Mobile

Email

O

Addresses

Name

Address

Tel Fax

Mobile

Email

Name

Address

Tel Fax

Mobile

Email

Name

Address

Tel Fax

Mobile

Email

Addresses

Name

Address

Tel Fax

Mobile

Email

Name

Address

Tel Fax

Mobile

Email

Addresses

Name

Address

Tel | Fax

Mobile

Email

Name

Address

Tel | Fax

Mobile

Email

Name

Address

Tel | Fax

Mobile

Email

Addresses

Name

Address

Tel Fax

Mobile

Email

Name

Address

Tel Fax

Mobile

Email

Name

Address

Tel Fax

Mobile

Email

Addresses

Name

Address

Tel Fax

Mobile

Email

Name

Address

Tel Fax

Mobile

Email

Name

Address

Tel Fax

Mobile

Email

Name

Address

Tel Fax

Mobile

Email

Name

Address

Tel Fax

Mobile

Email

P

Addresses

Name

Address

Tel Fax

Mobile

Email

Name

Address

Tel Fax

Mobile

Email

P

Addresses

Name

Address

Tel Fax

Mobile

Email

Name

Address

Tel Fax

Mobile

Email

Name

Address

Tel Fax

Mobile

Email

P

Addresses

Name

Address

Tel Fax

Mobile

Email

Name

Address

Tel Fax

Mobile

Email

Name

Address

Tel Fax

Mobile

Email

Addresses

Name

Address

Tel Fax

Mobile

Email

Name

Address

Tel Fax

Mobile

Email

Addresses

Name

Address

Tel Fax

Mobile

Email

Name

Address

Tel Fax

Mobile

Email

Name

Address

Tel Fax

Mobile

Email

Addresses

Name

Address

Tel Fax

Mobile

Email

Name

Address

Tel Fax

Mobile

Email

Name

Address

Tel Fax

Mobile

Email

Addresses

Name

Address

Tel Fax

Mobile

Email

Name

Address

Tel Fax

Mobile

Email

Name

Address

Tel Fax

Mobile

Email

Name

Address

Tel Fax

Mobile

Email

Name

Address

Tel Fax

Mobile

Email

Addresses

Name

Address

Tel Fax

Mobile

Email

R

HP

Addresses

Name

Address

Tel Fax

Mobile

Email

Name

Address

Tel Fax

Mobile

Email

Name

Address

Tel Fax

Mobile

Email

R

Addresses

Name

Address

Tel Fax

Mobile

Email

Name

Address

Tel Fax

Mobile

Email

Name

Address

Tel Fax

Mobile

Email

Addresses

Name

Address

Tel Fax

Mobile

Email

Name

Address

Tel Fax

Mobile

Email

Name

Address

Tel Fax

Mobile

Email

R

Addresses

Name
Address

Tel Fax
Mobile
Email

Name
Address

Tel Fax
Mobile
Email

Name
Address

Tel Fax
Mobile
Email

R

Addresses

Name

Address

Tel Fax

Mobile

Email

Name

Address

Tel Fax

Mobile

Email

S

Addresses

Name
Address

Tel Fax
Mobile
Email

Name
Address

Tel Fax
Mobile
Email

Name
Address

Tel Fax
Mobile
Email

S

Addresses

Name

Address

Tel Fax

Mobile

Email

Name

Address

Tel Fax

Mobile

Email

Name

Address

Tel Fax

Mobile

Email

S

Addresses

Name

Address

Tel Fax

Mobile

Email

Name

Address

Tel Fax

Mobile

Email

Name

Address

Tel Fax

Mobile

Email

Name

Address

Tel Fax

Mobile

Email

Name

Address

Tel Fax

Mobile

Email

S

Addresses

Name

Address

Tel Fax

Mobile

Email

Name

Address

Tel Fax

Mobile

Email

Addresses

Name

Address

Tel Fax

Mobile

Email

Name

Address

Tel Fax

Mobile

Email

Name

Address

Tel Fax

Mobile

Email

T

Addresses

Name

Address

Tel Fax

Mobile

Email

Name

Address

Tel Fax

Mobile

Email

Name

Address

Tel Fax

Mobile

Email

T

Addresses

Name

Address

Tel Fax

Mobile

Email

Name

Address

Tel Fax

Mobile

Email

T

Addresses

Name

Address

Tel Fax

Mobile

Email

Name

Address

Tel Fax

Mobile

Email

Name

Address

Tel Fax

Mobile

Email

T

Addresses

Name

Address

Tel Fax

Mobile

Email

Name

Address

Tel Fax

Mobile

Email

Name

Address

Tel Fax

Mobile

Email

T

Addresses

Name

Address

Tel Fax

Mobile

Email

Name

Address

Tel Fax

Mobile

Email

Name

Address

Tel Fax

Mobile

Email

T

Name

Address

Tel Fax

Mobile

Email

Name

Address

Tel Fax

Mobile

Email

Addresses

Name

Address

Tel | Fax

Mobile

Email

Addresses

Name

Address

Tel Fax

Mobile

Email

Name

Address

Tel Fax

Mobile

Email

Name

Address

Tel Fax

Mobile

Email

Addresses

Name

Address

Tel Fax

Mobile

Email

Name

Addresses

Tel Fax

Mobile

Email

Name

Addresses

Tel Fax

Mobile

Email

Addresses

Name

Address

Tel Fax

Mobile

Email

Name

Address

Tel Fax

Mobile

Email

Name

Address

Tel Fax

Mobile

Email

Addresses

Name

Address

Tel Fax

Mobile

Email

Name

Address

Tel Fax

Mobile

Email

Name

Address

Tel Fax

Mobile

Email

Addresses

Name

Address

Tel Fax

Mobile

Email

Name

Address

Tel Fax

Mobile

Email

Addresses

Name

Address

Tel Fax

Mobile

Email

Name

Address

Tel Fax

Mobile

Email

Name

Address

Tel Fax

Mobile

Email

Addresses

Name

Address

Tel Fax

Mobile

Email

Name

Address

Tel Fax

Mobile

Email

Name

Address

Tel Fax

Mobile

Email

Addresses

Name

Address

Tel Fax

Mobile

Email

Name

Address

Tel Fax

Mobile

Email

Name

Address

Tel Fax

Mobile

Email

Name

Address

Tel Fax

Mobile

Email

Name

Address

Tel Fax

Mobile

Email

Addresses

Name

Address

Tel Fax

Mobile

Email

Name

Address

Tel Fax

Mobile

Email

Addresses

Name

Address

Tel Fax

Mobile

Email

Name

Address

Tel Fax

Mobile

Email

Name

Address

Tel Fax

Mobile

Email

Addresses

Name

Address

Tel Fax

Mobile

Email

Name

Address

Tel Fax

Mobile

Email

Name

Address

Tel Fax

Mobile

Email

Addresses

Name

Address

Tel Fax

Mobile

Email

Name

Address

Tel Fax

Mobile

Email

Addresses

Name

Address

Tel Fax

Mobile

Email

Name

Address

Tel Fax

Mobile

Email

Name

Address

Tel Fax

Mobile

Email

Addresses

Name

Address

Tel Fax

Mobile

Email

Name

Address

Tel Fax

Mobile

Email

Name

Address

Tel Fax

Mobile

Email

NOTES

NOTES

NOTES